MY MAGNIFICENT
JELLY BEAN TREE

Maura Finn

Illustrated by Aura Parker

NEW FRONTIER PUBLISHING

If I had a jelly bean tree,
I would care for it while it was small.

Sprinkle on sugar,

And jugfuls of jam,

Then watch it grow sturdy and tall.

In the shade of my jelly bean tree,
I will wait 'til the beans look just right.

Then I'll wrap my
arms tightly
Around the tree's trunk ...
And shake it with all
of my might!

There'll be gurgling slurples and dribbly goo,
As I feast on the best of the crop.
Because fresh jelly beans are so juicy and plump.
(Not all dry like the ones from the shop.)

If I had a jelly bean tree,
I would build my house up in the sky.
Stretch out on my porch
In the afternoon sun,
As a river of clouds drift on by.

My magnificent jelly bean tree,
with a slide looping all the way round.

I'll go dizzily whizzing,

Past all of the bends,

Should I ever decide
to come down.

I will fend off intruders by day and by night,
Pesky creatures both feathered and furred.
Because jelly bean trees attract weasels and mice,
And a rather strange species of bird.

If I had a jelly bean tree,
I would measure a long piece of string.

Thread on yellow and green,
With some blue in between,

And I'd crown myself Jelly Bean King.

All alone in my jelly bean tree,
I will dance rudie nude in the rain.
And with all of this jelly
To use as shampoo,
I will never need bath time again.

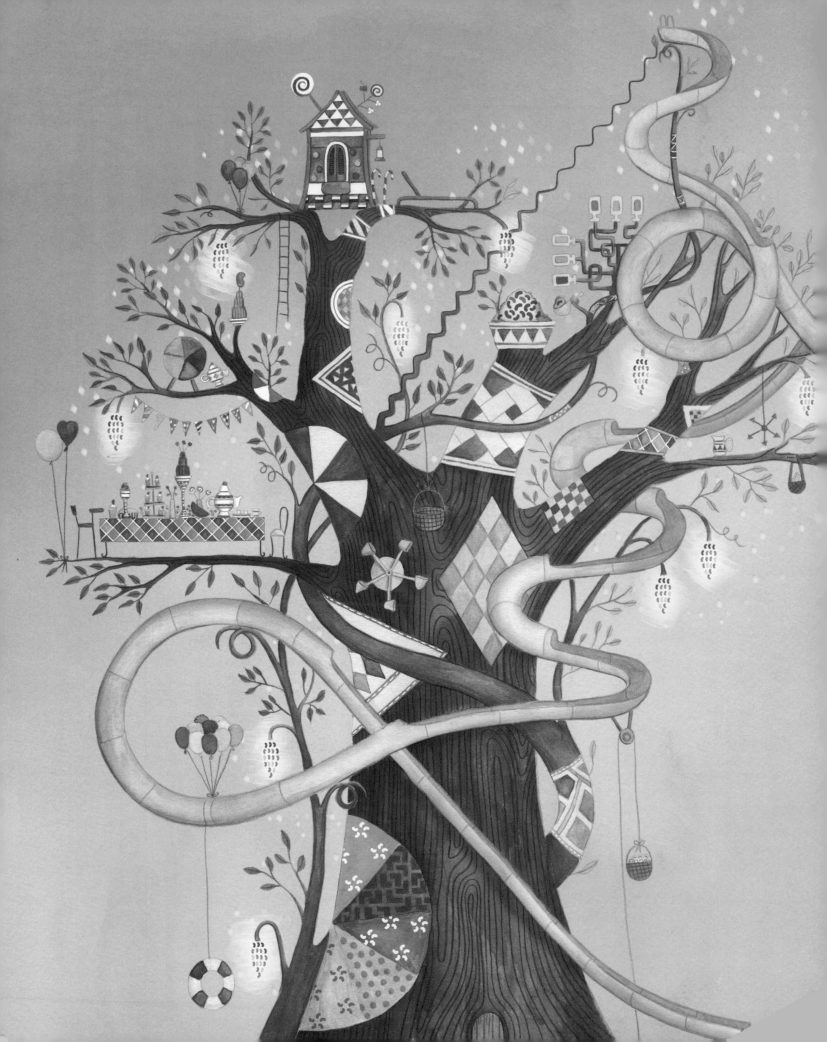

As the last of the sun trickles down from the sky,
What a breathtaking wonder I'll see.
Because jelly beans light up like lanterns at night!
Yet ...

There's no-one to see them but me.

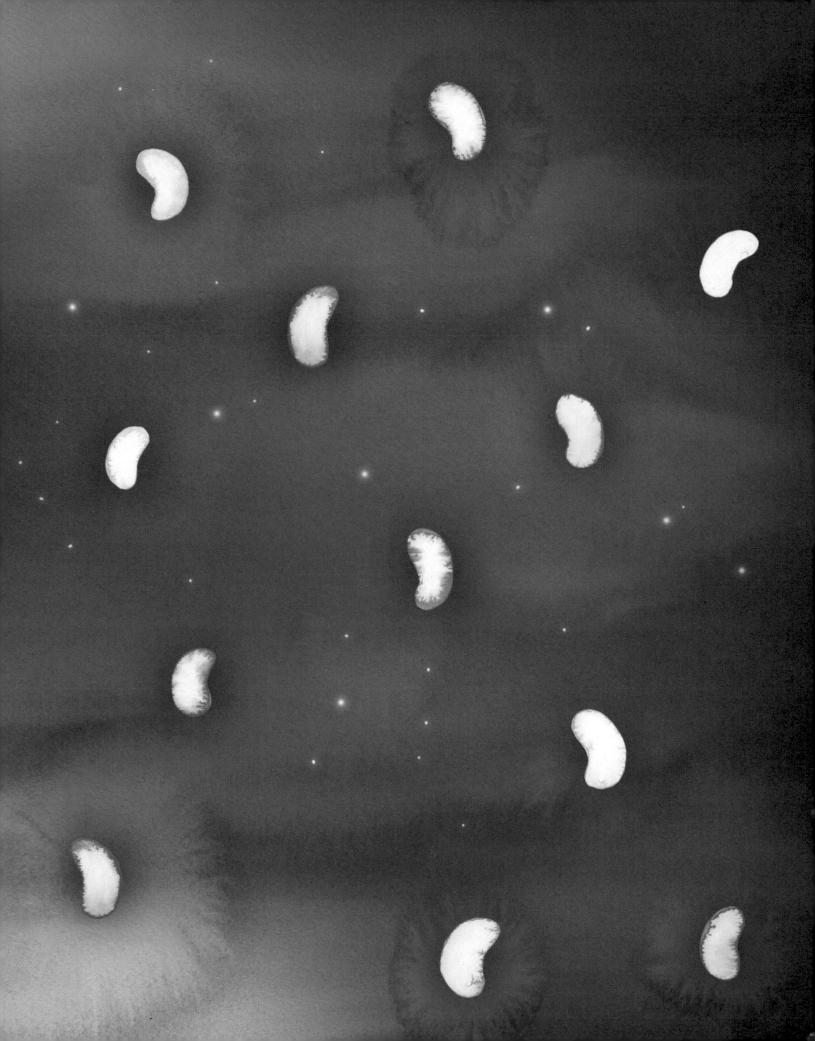

So,
If I had a jelly bean tree,
I would write to my family's address,

(Will you please come and visit?
Whenever you Choose.)

Then I'd send it by airmail express.

And, oh, all the fun we shall have,
In *our* marvellous jelly bean tree.
We'll make jelly bean pie,
Served with jelly bean cream,
And a large pot of jelly bean tea.

Some people say, 'Jelly beans don't grow on trees!'
I wonder, 'Well how do *they* know?'
Perhaps all their jelly beans failed to sprout ...

But my one has started to grow.